ROC

© 2006 by Faber Music Ltd
First published by Faber Music Ltd in 2006
3 Queen Square, London WC1N 3AU

Designed by Lydia Merrills-Ashcroft & Dominic Brookman
Edited by Lucy Holliday
Engraved by Emily King

Printed in England by Caligraving Ltd
All rights reserved

ISBN10: 0-571-52671-3
EAN13: 978-0-571-52671-0

To buy Faber Music publications
or to find out about the full range of titles available,
please contact your local music retailer
or Faber Music sales enquiries:

Faber Music Ltd, Burnt Mill, Elizabeth Way, Harlow, CM20 2HX England
Tel: +44(0)1279 82 89 82 Fax: +44(0)1279 82 89 83
sales@fabermusic.com fabermusic.com

# ALL DAY AND ALL OF THE NIGHT

### Words and Music by Raymond Davies

**Intro**       F | G F | B♭ G F | G F | B♭ G F ‖

**Verse 1**

         G     F     B♭     G      F  G  F B♭ G F

I'm not content to be with you in the day - time.

        G   F     B♭     G     F G   F B♭ G

Girl, I want to be with you all of the time.

          B♭        F             A  A/G  A/C  A

The only time I feel alright is by your side.

**Chorus 1**

        D   C     F     D       C D

Girl, I want to be with you all of the time,

          C       F        D C

All day and all of the night,

        D   C     F       D  C D

All day and all of the night.

          C       F        D C

All day and all of the night.

**Verse 2**

        G  F       B♭     G      F G   F B♭ G F

I believe that you and me last for - ever.

         G     F     B♭     G         F/G  F B♭ G F

All year, all day and night time yours leave me never.

          B♭         F            A  A/G  A/C  A

The only time I feel alright is by your side.

**Chorus 2**
```
        D     C     F      D  C    D
Girl, I  want to be with you all of the time,

        C      F        D  C  D
All day and all of the night,

        C      F       D  C D C F F D          D
All day and all of the night._____  Oh! Come on!
```

**Guitar solo**
```
                                        x2
‖: G  F | B♭  G  F | G  F | B♭  G  F :‖

| G  F | B♭  G  F |
```

**Verse 3**
```
G  F         B♭       G          F G  F B♭ G F
I believe that you and me last for - ev - er.

   G      F      B♭      G          F  G F B♭ G
All year, all day and night time yours leave me ne - ver.

F   B♭       F                    A   A/G A/C A
The only time I feel alright is by your side.
```

**Chorus 3**
```
D     C     F      D          C  D
Girl, I want to be with you all of the time,

     C      F       D  C  D
All day and all of the night,

     C      F       D  C
All day and all of the night.

D  C      F       D    D C F D ‖
All day and all of the night.
```

# ANOTHER BRICK IN THE WALL (PART 2)

Words and Music by George Roger Waters

**Verse 1**

Dm        Dm        Dm        Dm
We don't need no education.

Dm        Dm        Dm        Dm
We don't need no thought control.

Dm        Dm        Dm        Dm
No dark sarcasm in the classroom.

Dm        Dm        G        G
Teacher leave them kids alone.

G        G        Dm
Hey teacher! Leave them kids alone.

F        C        Dm        Dm
All in all it's just a - nother brick in the wall.

F        C        N.C.        N.C.
All in all you're just a - nother brick in the wall.

**Verse 2**

N.C.        N.C.        Dm        Dm
We don't need no education.

Dm        Dm        Dm        Dm
We don't need no thought control.

Dm        Dm        Dm        Dm
No dark sarcasm in the classrooms.

Dm        Dm        G        G
Teachers leave them kids alone.

**cont.**

```
       G   G                        Dm  C/D  Dm  C/A  G
       Hey teacher! Leave those kids alone.

       F                    C              Dm       Dm
       All in  all  you're  just  a-nother brick in the  wall.

       F                    C              Dm       Dm
       All in  all  you're  just  a-nother brick in the  wall.
```

**Guitar solo**

```
          Dm      Dm      Dm      Dm      Dm      Dm      Dm      Dm

          Am7/D  Am7/D   Dm7     Dm7     C/D     C/D     Dm      Dm

          G/D    G/D     Dm7     Dm7     G/D     G/D     Dm      Dm

          C/D    C/D     B♭/D    B♭/D    C/D     C/D

          N.C.        Voices, drums, effects to fade
```

# ALL YOU GOOD, GOOD PEOPLE

Words and Music by Daniel McNamara and Richard McNamara

**Intro**  | N.C. | F# | B | F# | E | E | B | F# | B ‖

**Verse I**
F#
I feel like I'm at something,

     B
You always say you need more time.

F#          E                  E
  Well I'll stay right here and I'll wait for good

          B              F# B
Until I find a love worth mine.

        F#
Some day you've got it coming,

          B                F#
It hurts me when I read the signs

    E                    E
So loud and clear that I'll make you glad if I'm

B           F#      F#
Leaving first and crying.

**Chorus I**
  E                B
  All you good, good people, listen to me.

F#                   F#
  You're just about done with the way that you feel.

E                  B
  'Cos nothing rings home enough to dig your heels in,

F#                 F#
  You don't have to leave me to see what I mean.

E                B       F#  B
  All you good, good people, listen to me.

**Instrumental** ‖:F♯ | B | F♯ | E | E | B | F♯ | B :‖

| F♯ | B | F♯ | E | E | B | F♯ | F♯ |

**Break**
       E           D            F♯                 F♯
And all I wanna do  is find my name upon the line,

       E              D                 F♯   F♯
Be - fore I have to lose this I want time._____

**Chorus 2**
E                        B
    All you good, good people, listen to me.

F♯                   F♯
    You're just about done with the way that you feel.

E                     B
    'Cos nothing rings home enough to dig your heels in,

F♯                      F♯
    You don't have to leave me to see what I mean.

E                     B
    Lose all your fears, they're keeping you down,

F♯                    F♯
    You won't have to fake it while I'm around.

E                     B           F♯   B⁷
    All you good, good people, listen to me.

**Outro**

F#                 B                 F#     B

La la la la____ la la la la la.

F#                 B                 F#               B

La la la la____ la la la la la____ yeah yeah yeah.

| F# | B | F# | B | B | B | B | B |

‖: F#            B                F#         B      **x4** :‖

La la la la____ la la la la____ la la la la____ la.

‖: F# | B | F# | B **x3** :‖

| F# | B | F# ‖

# CATCH THE SUN

Words and Music by Jimi Goodwin, Jez Williams and Andy Williams

**Verse I**

B
Ev'ry day it comes to this

B
Catch the things you might have missed.

Em⁹                                    B
You say,___ "Get back to yesterday."___

B
I ain't ever going back,

B
Back to the place that I can't stand,

Em⁹                              B    B⁷sus⁴
But I,___ I miss the way you lie.

          B
'Cause I've always been misunderstood,

B
Pulled apart and ripped in two,

Em⁹                              F#add¹¹
But I,___ I miss the way you lie.

Gmaj⁷    Dmaj⁷  Amaj⁷         Emaj⁷
**Chorus I**  Catch the sun        before it's gone.

Gmaj⁷    Dmaj⁷  Amaj⁷         Emaj⁷
Here it comes, up in smoke and gone.

**cont.**

Gmaj⁷     Dmaj⁷    Amaj⁷    Emaj⁷
Catch the sun,       it never____ comes.

Gmaj⁷         Dmaj⁷  Amaj⁷         Emaj⁷  B  B  B⁷sus⁴
Cry in the sand,____   Lost ev'rything I____ had.

**Verse 2**

B
'Cause I never really understood,

B
Why I did not feel so good,

    Em⁹                    B  B⁷sus⁴
But I,____  I miss the way you lie.

      B
'Cause I've always been up and down,

B
Never wanted to hit the ground

    Em⁹   Em⁹            F♯add¹¹
But I,____ I miss the way you lie.

**Chorus 2**

Gmaj⁷       Dmaj⁷  Amaj⁷   Emaj⁷
Catch the sun____ before it's____ gone.

Gmaj⁷  Dmaj⁷  Amaj⁷         Emaj⁷
Here it comes, up in smoke and____ gone.

**cont.**

Gmaj⁷        Dmaj⁷  Amaj⁷       Emaj⁷
Catch the sun,_____ it never____ comes.

Gmaj⁷        Dmaj⁷  Amaj⁷           Emaj⁷  B
Cry in the sand,_____ lost ev'rything I____ had.

**Instrumental** | B | Em | B | Em | F♯ | G | A | B | Badd¹¹ |

‖: Gmaj⁷ | Dmaj⁷ | Amaj⁷ | Emaj⁷ :‖

**Chorus 3**

Gmaj⁷        Dmaj⁷  Amaj⁷      Emaj⁷
Catch the sun____ before it's____ gone.

Gmaj⁷  Dmaj⁷  Amaj⁷           Emaj⁷
Here it comes,   up in smoke and____ gone.

Gmaj⁷        Dmaj⁷  Amaj⁷     Emaj⁷
Catch the sun,____ it never____ comes.

Gmaj⁷        Dmaj⁷  Amaj⁷          Emaj⁷
Cry in the sand,_____ lost ev'rything I____ had.

**Outro**

                              *x6*
‖: Gmaj⁷ | Dmaj⁷ | Amaj⁷ | Emaj⁷ :‖  Gmaj⁷  ‖

# DON'T LOOK BACK INTO THE SUN

### Words and Music by Peter Doherty and Carl Barât

**Intro**      | G  | D  | Em | D  | C  | D  | G | D/G |

                | G  | G/D | G/E | G/D | C/D | G/D | G | G/D |

                |G  | D  | Em | D  | C  | D  | G | D ‖

**Verse 1**
```
         G                   D
Don't look back in - to the sun,

  Em                        D
 Now you know that the time has come.

C                D          G          D
And they said it would never come for you. Ah, uh, uh, oh.

G                      D
Oh my friend you haven't changed,

  Em                         D
 You're looking rough and living strange.

            C          D          G            D
And I know you've got a taste for it too. Ah, uh, uh, oh.
```

**Chorus 1**
```
       C                                      G
They'll never forgive you but they won't let you go, oh no.

       C                              D N.C. D N.C.
She'll never forgive you but she won't let you go, oh no.
```

**Verse 2**

   G                  D
Don't look back in - to the sun,

            Em                        D
You've cast your pearls but you're on the run.

       C             D                G
And all the lies you said, who did you say?

D           G                   D
  But then they played that song at the death dis - co,

           Em            D
It  start - ed fast but it ends so slow.

       C               D             G    D
And all that time just reminded me of you.

**Chorus 2**    *As Chorus 1*

...go *(let me go!)*

**Guitar solo**   ‖: G | D | Em | D | C | D | G | D :‖ *x2*

**Chorus 3**    *As Chorus 2*

**Outro**    ‖: G | D | Em | D | C | D | G | D :‖ *x2*

       | G | D | Em | D | C | D | G ‖

# EVER FALLEN IN LOVE
# (WITH SOMEONE YOU SHOULDN'T'VE)

### Words and Music by Peter Shelley

**Intro**  |C#m  |C#m  B |C#m  |C#m  B/D# |E  |E  |E  |E

**Verse 1**
       C#m                                B
You spurn my natural emotions,

       C#m                    B/D#  E
You make me feel I'm dirt and I'm   hurt.

       C#m                 B/D#
And if I start a commotion,

       C#m                        B/D#  E
I'll run the risk of losing you and that's worse.

**Chorus 1**
       C#m                 B
Ever fallen in love with someone,

       B/D#   C#m               B
Ever fallen in love, in love with someone,

       B/D#     D              A
Ever fallen in love, in love with someone you

                        B  E  B  E  B
Shouldn't have fallen in love with?

**Verse 2**

C#m                                                    B/D#
I can't see much of the future,

C#m                          B/D#              E
Unless we find what's to blame, what a shame

C#m                                                 B
And we won't be together much longer,


**Chorus 2**     *As Chorus 1*


**Verse 3**      *As Verse 1*


**Chorus 3**     *As Chorus 1*


**Link**     ‖:E    |E    |E    |E    :‖E    |E    |E


**Chorus 4**     *As Chorus 1*


                          A      D  A  D  A
**Outro**     A - fallen in love with?

                                      B
Ever fallen in love with someone you

                                      E          ‖
Shouldn't have fallen in love with?

# CRASH

**Words and Music by Paul Court, Stephen Dullaghan and Tracy Spencer**

**Intro**  | B | E/B | F#/B | E/B | B | E/B | F#/B ‖

**Verse I**

E   N.C.       B     E
Here you go,— way too fast,

      F#                    E
If you don't slow down you're gonna crash.

          B         E
You should watch, watch your step

       F#              E
If you don't look out, gonna break your neck.

**Pre-chorus I**

      B         E
So shut, shut your mouth, 'cause

F#             E
I'm not listening anyhow I've had

 B         E
Enough, enough of you,

   F#         E
Enough to last a lifetime through.

**Chorus I**

      F#sus4
So what do you want of me?

       B        E
I've got no words of sympathy.

               F#sus⁴

**cont.**      And if I go around with you,

            B              E              F#sus⁴   F#sus⁴

        You know that I'll get messed up too with you.

        B            E           F#  E

**Link**      Na na na na na  na na na na na na.____

        B            E           F#  E

        Na na na na na  na na na na na na.____

      E            B          E

**Verse 2**     Here you go,__ way too fast,

              F#                          E

        (If you) don't slow down you're gonna crash.

           B              E

        You don't know what's been going down,

      F#                      E

        You've been running all over town.

**Pre-chorus 2**  *As Pre-chorus I*

               F#sus⁴

**Chorus 2**     So what do you want of me,

        B           E

        I've got no cure for misery.

**cont.**

F#sus⁴

And if I go around with you,

B     E       F#sus⁴

You know that I'll get messed up too with you.

F#sus⁴

With you, with you...

**Outro**

‖: B     E

Na na na na na  na na na na  na na na

*Repeat to fade*

F#         E  :‖

Slow down, you're gonna crash.

# FAT BOTTOMED GIRLS

Words and Music by Brian May

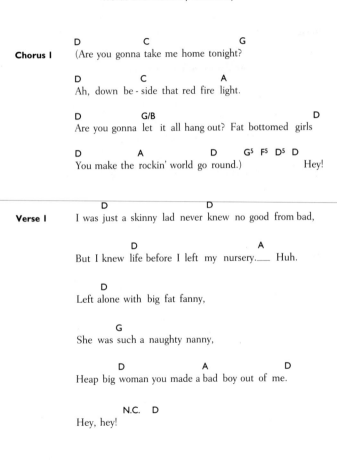

**Chorus 1**

      D           C               G
(Are you gonna take me home tonight?

      D           C             A
Ah, down be - side that red fire light.

      D           G/B                         D
Are you gonna let it all hang out? Fat bottomed girls

      D         A           D   G⁵ F⁵ D⁵ D
You make the rockin' world go round.)        Hey!

**Verse 1**

             D                    D
I was just a skinny lad never knew no good from bad,

               D               A
But I knew life before I left my nursery.___ Huh.

      D
Left alone with big fat fanny,

      G
She was such a naughty nanny,

         D          A          D
Heap big woman you made a bad boy out of me.

         N.C.  D
Hey, hey!

**Verse 2**

N.C.     D
I've been singin' with my band

'Cross the water, 'cross the land,

                            A
I seen ev'ry blue eyed floozy on the way.— Hey.

       D                                      G
But their beauty and their style went kind of smooth

                  D         A
After a while, take me to them dirty ladies ev'ry time.

Come on!

**Chorus 2**

D           C                    G/B
Oh won't you take me home tonight.

D           C            G/B  A
Oh down beside your red fire light.

D           G                                D
Oh and you give it all you've got, fat bottomed girls

               A             D     G
You make the rockin' world go round.

                    D       A         D
Fat bottomed girls, you make the rockin' world go round.

**Link**  |D  G/F | G/B  D | G  D | A  G ‖

Hey listen here, ah.

           D                                 D
**Verse 3**    Now I got mortgages and homes, I got stiffness in my bones,

           D                         A
Ain't no beauty queens in this locality.__ I tell ya.

           D                          G
Oh but I_ still get my pleasure, still got my greatest treasure,

           D                 A            D
Heap big woman, you gonna make a big man of me.

           G/D
Now get this.__

           C  G/B
**Chorus 3**    Oh I know.__ Please! *(Are you gonna take me home tonight?)*

D             C         G/B  A
Oh down beside__ that red fire light.

D          G                       D
Oh you gonna let it all hang out, fat bottomed girls

           A             D   G
You make the rockin' world go round, yeah,

               D         A          D  ‖
Fat bottomed girls, you make the rockin' world go round.

# HOLIDAY

Words and Music by Billie Joe Armstrong,
Michael Pritchard and Frank E. Wright III

**Intro**  | Fm D♭ | A♭ E♭ | Fm D♭ | A♭ E♭ ‖ Fm D♭| A♭ E♭

Say,

| Fm D♭ | A♭ E♭ | F5 D♭5 | A♭5 E♭5 | F5 D♭5 | A♭5 E♭5 ‖

hey!

F5     D♭5     A♭5  E♭5

**Verse 1**  Hear the sound of the falling rain

F5     D♭5     A♭5  C5   F5

Coming down like an Arma - geddon flame.

D♭5

(Hey) the shame,

A♭5   E♭5    C5     C5

The ones who died with - out a name.___

F5     D♭5     A♭5  E♭5

Hear the dogs howling out of key

F5     D♭5     A♭5   C5

To a hymn called 'Faith and Misery,'

F5     D♭5

(Hey) and bleed,

A♭5   E♭5   C5    C5

The company lost the war today.___

F5    D♭5

**Chorus 1**  I beg to dream and differ

A♭5       E♭5

From the hollow lies.

F5     D♭5     A♭5   C5   (N.C.)

This is the dawning of the rest of our lives___ on holiday.

**Link I**   | Fm | D♭ | A♭ | E♭ | Fm | D♭ | A♭ | E♭ |

 

            F5             D♭5           A♭5    E♭5

**Verse 2**   Hear the drum pounding out of time,

             F5             D♭5     A♭5     C5         F5

     Another protest - or has crossed the line

                  D♭5

     (Hey) to find

              A♭5     E♭5    C5        C5

     The money's on the other side.___

          F5        D♭5    A♭5     E♭5     F5

     Can I get another Amen? *(Amen)*

                D♭5          A♭5     C5       F5

     There's a flag wrapped around a score of men.

                D♭5

     (Hey) a gag,

        A♭5     E♭5     C5         C5

     A plastic bag on a monument.___

           F5        D♭5

**Chorus 2**   I beg to dream and differ

         A♭5                E♭5

From the hollow lies.___

         F5        D♭5         A♭5     C5     (N.C.)

This is the dawning of the rest of our lives__ on holiday.

**Link 2**   ‖: F⁵  A♭⁵ | D♭⁵  B♭⁵ | E♭⁵  C⁵ | F⁵  A♭⁵ | E♭⁵  C⁵  F⁵  :‖ **x2**

Hey! *(1° only)*

**Guitar solo**   | D♭⁵ | A♭ | C | F♭  E♭ | D♭  | A♭  | C | C | C | C |

**Link 3**   | F  A♭ | D♭  B♭  E♭  C | F  A♭ | E♭  C  F |

**Bridge**

F   A♭      D♭      B♭        E♭      C      F
The repre - sentative  from Cali - fornia

        A♭    E♭    C    F
has the floor.

F       A♭             D♭    B♭   E♭    C
Zieg  Heil  to the Presi - dent  gas - man,

F            A♭           E♭      C   F
Bombs  a - way is your puni - ish - ment.

F        A♭          D♭   B♭  E♭      C
Pulverize the Eif - fel  Tow - ers,

F            A♭           E♭     C    F
Who criticize your gov - ern - ment.

F        A♭             D♭   B♭  E♭    C
Bang, bang goes the bro - ken  glass and

F                A♭          E     C   F
Kill  all the fags that don't a - gree.

**cont.**

    F           A$\flat$  D$\flat$  B$\flat$  E$\flat$  C
Trials by fire set - ting fire___

F          A$\flat$     E$\flat$    C  F  B$\flat$
Is not a way that's meant for me.

C             C  B$\flat$  C
Just 'cause      *(Hey, hey, hey, hey)*

C             C
Just 'cause, because we're outlaws, yeah.

*(Hey, hey, hey, hey.)*

**Chorus 3**

F$^5$        D$\flat$$^5$          A$\flat$$^5$         E$\flat$$^5$
I beg to dream and differ from the hollow lies.

F$^5$        D$\flat$$^5$       A$\flat$$^5$    C$^5$
This is the dawning of the rest of our lives.___

F$^5$        D$\flat$$^5$        A$\flat$$^5$       E$\flat$$^5$
I beg to dream and differ from the hollow lies.

F$^5$        D$\flat$$^5$       A$\flat$$^5$     C$^5$   C$^5$
This is the dawning of the rest of our lives,_____

C$^5$            C$^5$    (Fm)
This is our lives  on holiday.

**Outro**  | Fm  D$\flat$ | A$\flat$  E$\flat$ | Fm  D$\flat$ | A$\flat$  E$\flat$ |

  | Fm  D$\flat$ | A$\flat$$^5$  E$\flat$$^5$ | Fm  D$\flat$ | E$\flat$$^5$  C$^5$ | F$^5$  F$^5$ ‖

# HOUND DOG

Words and Music by Jerry Leiber and Mike Stoller

**Verse 1**

N.C.
You ain't nothin' but a

C
Hound Dog, cryin' all the time.

C
You ain't nothin' but a

F        F⁷
Hound Dog, cryin' all the time.

            G
Well you ain't never caught a rabbit

       F           C   N.C.
And you ain't no friend of mine.

**Verse 2**

N.C.
When they said you was

   C                      C
High - classed, well that was just a lie.

When they said you was

      F        F⁷             C
High - classed, well that was just a lie.

          G
Well you ain't never caught a rabbit

      F          C   N.C.
And you ain't no friend of mine.

**Verse 3**    *As Verse 1*

**Guitar solo 1** | N.C. | C | C | C | C | F | F | C |

|| C | G⁷ | F⁷ | C ||

**Verse 4**    *As Verse 2*

**Guitar solo 2** *As Guitar solo 1*

**Verse 5**    *As Verse 2*

 

            N.C.
**Verse 6**    You ain't nothin' but a

            C
Hound Dog, cryin' all the time.

            C
You ain't nothin' but a

            F          F⁷        C
Hound Dog, cryin' all the time.

                G          N.C.
Well, you ain't never caught a rabbit,

        N.C.              D♭⁶/⁹  C⁶ ||
You ain't no friend of mine.

# HOUNDS OF LOVE

Words and Music by Kate Bush

**Verse I**

A⁵        E⁵        D⁵
When I was a child___ running in the night,

      C#⁵
I was af - raid of what might be.

A⁵       E⁵
Hiding in the dark and hiding on the

  D⁵      C#⁵
Streets for, and of what was following me.

**Chorus I**

F#m     E     D     C#m
   Oh oh, oh oh oh, the hounds of love are calling.

F#m     D     C#m     E
   Oh oh, oh oh oh, I've always been a coward.

F#m     D
   Oh oh, oh oh oh,

C#m     Bm     C#m     F#m
And I don't know what's good for me.

**Verse 2**

      A⁵ E⁵     D⁵        C#⁵
Well here I go, it's coming at me through the tree,

A⁵     E⁵       D⁵   C#⁵
Help me someone, help me please.

A⁵     E⁵       D⁵
Take your shoes off and I will throw them in the lake,

       C$^{\#5}$            A$^5$  E$^5$                 D$^5$    C$^{\#5}$

**cont.**    And I will be___ two steps on the water.

       A$^5$         E$^5$          D$^5$

I found a fox caught by dogs,

              C$^{\#5}$           A$^5$

He let me take him in my hands.

       E$^5$            D$^5$          C$^{\#5}$

His little heart, it beat so fast that I am ashamed to be

           A$^5$           E$^5$

Running away___ from nothing real,

          D$^5$          C$^{\#5}$              F$^{\#}$m

I just can't deal with this, I  feel ashamed to be there.

       F$^{\#}$m         E          D          C$^{\#}$m

**Chorus 2**    Oh oh, oh oh oh, amongst your hounds of loving,

       F$^{\#}$m       D       C$^{\#}$m           E            F$^{\#}$m

Oh oh, oh oh oh, I  feel your arms surrounding me.

          D          C$^{\#}$m       E

Oh oh, oh oh oh, I've always been a coward,

       F$^{\#}$m       D        C$^{\#}$m       Bm       C$^{\#}$m    F$^{\#}$m

Oh oh, oh oh oh, and I don't know what's good for me.

**Verse 3**

           A   E            D   C#m
Well here I go,__ don't let me go, hold me down,

A        E                  D   C#m
It's coming at me through the trees.

A        E            D      C#m
Help me some - one, help me please,

A        E               D
Take my shoes off, and I will throw them in the lake.

C#m         A   E            D    C#m
And I will be__ two__ steps on the water.

A                   E
And do you know what I need, do you know what I

D          C#m
Need? I need a hi - ya - yuh - yuh - yuh - yuh - yuh.

A  E  D  C#m  A       E
                Take my shoes off and I will

D              C#m           A
Throw them in the lake,__ and I will be__

E               D⁵  C#m  A  E  D  C#m
Two steps on the water.

**Outro**

```
A                       E
I don't know what's  good for me,

                        D            C#m
I don't know what's  good for me.

A                       E
And do you  know what I  need, do you  know what I

D                 C#m                              A  ‖
Need?  I  need  a  hi - ya - yuh - yuh - yuh - yuh - yuh - yuh.
```

# THE KILLING MOON

Words and Music by Ian McCulloch, William Sergeant,
Leslie Pattinson and Pete De Freitas

**Intro**  ‖: Bm | Bm/A | G | G :‖ Em | Em | C | C ‖

**Verse 1**
             Em
Under____blue moon  I  saw  you

          C                  Em
So soon you'll take  me  up in your arms

Too  late  to beg you or

   C
Cancel it though I  know  it  must be the

   Em            C
Killing time  un - willingly  mine.

**Chorus 1**
    G  Cm                 G Cm                      G
Fate    up against your will____ through the thick and thin

    Cm            G  Cm              G   Cm
You will  wait until____ you give yourself to him.____

**Link 1**  | Em | Em | C | C |

**Verse 2**

           Em                     C
In starlit nights I saw you so cruelly you kissed me

             Em              C
Your lips a magic world___your sky all hung with jewels

           Em          C
The killing moon will come too soon.

**Chorus 2**

      G  Cm              G  Cm                      G
Fate   up against your will       through thick and thin___

      Cm             G  Cm               G     Cm
He will wait until_____you give yourself to him._____

---

**Instrumental** ‖: Bm  Bm/A  G  Em :‖ *x3*    Bm  B/A  G  D

**Link 2**      *As Link 1*

**Verse 3**     *As Verse 1*

**Chorus 3**    ‖: *As Chorus 2* :‖ *Repeat to fade*

# LAST NITE

### Words and Music by Julian Casablancas

**Intro**    C  ‖: F5/C  |  C5 :‖: F5  |  C5/G :‖

**Verse I**

          C
Last  night she said "Oh baby I

Dm9            G                  Em7       G/D
Feel so down, oh it turns me off, when I feel left out."

       C                    Dm9
So I, I turn round, "Oh baby don't care no more,

       G            Em7
I know this for sure, I'm walking out that door."

G/D     C
Well I've been in town for just now fifteen whole minutes

               Dm9               G
Now, oh baby I feel so down and I don't know why

       Em7         G/D
I keep walking for miles.

**Chorus I**

          F5                   C5/G
And see people they don't understand.

     F5                    C5/G
No girlfriends they can't understand.

      F5                  C5/G
Your grandsons they won't understand.

     F5                            C5/G
On top of this I ain't ever gonna understand.

**Verse 2**

        C
Last nite she said "Oh baby don't

Dm⁹               G                  Em⁷       G/D
Feel so down, oh it turns me off, when I feel left out."

      C                             Dm⁹
So I, I turn round, "Oh baby gonna be alright."

          G              Em⁷            G/D
It was a great big lie, 'cause I left that night, yeah.

**Link**        C   ‖: F⁵ | C⁵/G :‖

---

**Guitar solo**   C | C | F | F | G | G ‖

           F⁵                          C⁵/G
**Chorus 2**  Oh people they don't understand.

           F⁵                        C⁵/G
No girlfriends they don't understand.

         F⁵                          C⁵/G
In spaceships they won't understand.

         F⁵                             C⁵/G   N.C.
And me I ain't ever gonna understand.

**Verse 3**

        C
Last nite she said "Oh baby don't

Dm$^9$                G                      Em$^7$       G/D
Feel so down, oh it turns me off, when I feel left out."

      C                                  Dm$^9$
So I, I turn round, "Oh little girl I don't care no more,

        G                        Em$^7$       G/D
I know this for sure I'm walking out that door."

     C    ‖: F$^5$   C$^5$/G :‖  C ‖

**Outro**      Yeah.

# LIVIN' ON A PRAYER

Words and Music by Desmond Child, Jon Bon Jovi and Richie Sambora

**Intro**  | Esus² | Esus² | Em | Em | C/E | D/E | Em |

                        C/E                      D/E         Em
         *(Spoken)*   *(Once upon a time,   not so long ago...)*

        Em                                 Esus²

**Verse 1**   Tommy used to work on the docks,

        Em
        Union's been on strike, he's down on his luck,

          C         D      Em
        It's tough, so tough.___

        Em                              Esus²
        Gina works the diner all day

        Em
        Working for her man, she brings home her pay,

          C     D     Em
        For love, for love.

        Em                C    D              Em

**Pre-chorus 1**  She says we've got to hold on to what we've got.

          C            D                 Em
        It doesn't make a diff'rence if we make it or not.

           C       D          Em    C
        We've got each other and that's a lot for love.

           D
        We'll give it a shot.

|          | Em      C      D |
|----------|------------------|
| **Chorus I** | Woah, we're halfway there. |

Em      C     D
**Chorus I**  Woah, we're halfway there.

G   C D
Woah,  livin' on a prayer.

Em     C       D
Take my hand, we'll make it, I swear.

G   C D          Em
Woah,  livin' on a prayer.

**Link I**    Em

           Em
**Verse 2**  Tommy's got his six - string in hock,

Esus² Em
Now he's holding in what he used to make it talk.

    C   D   Em
So tough, it's tough.___

Em
Gina dreams of running away;

Esus² Em
When she cries in the night, Tommy whispers:

       C    D      Em
"Baby it's ok,  someday."

            Em       C D          Em
**Pre-chorus 2** We've got to hold on to what we've got.

         C            D              Em
It doesn't make a diff'rence if we make it or not.

        C       D               Em   C

**cont.**    We've got each other and that's a lot for love.

        D

We'll give it a shot.

        Em   C    D

**Chorus 2**    Woah, we're halfway there.

        G    C D

Woah,   livin' on a prayer.

        Em     C       D

Take my hand, we'll make it, I swear.

        G    C D              C   C/E   C/B

Woah,   livin' on a prayer.___ Livin' on a prayer.

                          x3

**Guitar solo**  ‖: Em | C | D :‖ G C Em

        Em             C   D           Em   D

**Pre-chorus 3**  Oh, we've got to hold on, ready or not,

         C                   D

You live for the fight when it's all that you've got.

        ‖: Gm   E♭     F

**Chorus 4**    Woah, we're halfway there.

        B♭    E♭   F

Woah,   livin' on a prayer.

        Gm       E♭        F

Take my hand and we'll make it, I swear.

                   *Repeat to fade*

        B♭    E♭   F                 :‖

Woah,   livin' on a prayer.

# MAKE ME SMILE (COME UP AND SEE ME)

Words and Music by Steve Harley

**Intro**        G

                N.C.              F      C            G

**Verse 1**    You've done it all, you've broken ev'ry code.

                F                C       G

                And pulled the rebel to the  floor.___

                                F      C              G

                You've spoilt the game, no matter what you say.

                F                C          G

                For only metal, what a bore.

                F          C        F        C    G

                Blue eyes, blue eyes, how can you tell so many lies?

                Dm                F          C   G

**Chorus 1**   Come up and see me, make me  smile.___

                Dm                      F       C   G  N.C.

                I'll do what you want, running wild.___

                N.C.             F      C              G

**Verse 2**    There's nothing left, all's gone and run away.___

                F                C   G

                Maybe you'll tarry for a while.___

                        F      C            G

              It's just a test, a game for us to play.___

                F          C        G

                Win or lose, it's hard  to smile.___

                F        C        F          C        G

                Resist, resist. It's from yourself you have to hide.

**Chorus 2**   *As Chorus 1*

**Guitar solo**   | F | Em | F | Am | Em | Em | G⁷ | G⁷ ‖: Dm   F   C   G :‖ G N.C.

           N.C.          F        C             G
**Verse 3**   There ain't no  more,you've taken  ev'rything__

        F        C       G
     From my belief in Mother  Earth.__

              F      C        G
  Can  you  ignore  my  faith  in  ev'rything?

       F               C            G
     'Cause I  know  what  faith  is,  and  what  it's  worth.

       F     C  F          C        G
     Away, away.  And don't say  maybe you'll try.

**Chorus 3**   *As Chorus 1*

       F   C        F   C          G
**Bridge 1**   Ooh, ooh  la la la,  ooh,  ooh  la la la,   ooooh - ah.

**Chorus 4**   *As Chorus 1*

**Bridge 2**   *As Bridge 1*

**Chorus 5**   *As Chorus 1 (to fade)*

# MORE THAN A FEELING

Words and Music by Ton Scholz

**Intro**   ‖: D  Dsus⁴  D │ C  G/B  G :‖ **x4**

**Verse I**

    D               Dsus⁴  D
I woke up this morning and

C          G/B    G
The sun was gone,

D              Dsus⁴  D  C       G/B  G
Turned on some music  to start my day

   D    Dsus⁴  D     C  G/B  G
I lost myself in  a fam - iliar song.

   D        Dsus⁴  D  Cadd⁹      G/B
I closed my eyes and I slipped away.

**Link I**   Am  Em/G │ D    │

**Chorus I**   G  C │ Em  D │ G  C │ Em  D

   G               C    Em            D
It's more than a feel - ing *(more than a feel - ing)*

When I hear old song they used to play,___

Em            D
*(More than a feel - ing)*

**cont.**

G           C           Em           D
I begin dream - ing___ *(more than a feel - ing)*

G           C         E♭
'Til I see Mary Ann walk a - way,

Em⁷          A
I see my Mary Ann walkin' away.

**Link 2**    | D  Cadd⁹ | G/B  G |

               | D⁵  Cadd⁹ | G/B  G ‖

**Verse 2**

D      Dsus⁴ D    Cadd⁹    G/B  G
So many people have come and gone,

D      Dsus⁴ D    C    G/B  G
The faces fade as the years go by;

D      Dsus⁴ D    Cadd⁹    G/B  G
Yet I still recall as I wonder on,

D      Dsus⁴ D    Cadd⁹    G/B
As clear as the sun in the summer sky.

**Link 3**    | Am  Em/G | D ‖

**Chorus 2**    | G  C | Em  D | G  C | Em  D |

G           C           Em           D
It's more than a feel - ing,___ *(more than a feel - ing)*

**cont.**

        G              C        Em
When I hear that old song they used to play,

                D
*(More than a feel - ing)*

  G             C        Em                D
I begin dream - ing___ *(more than a feel - ing)*

     G          C      E♭
'Til I see Mary Ann walk a - way,

Em⁷             A            |Bm  A  G  D/F♯ |Asus⁴ A  |
 I see my Mary Ann walkin' away.

**Guitar solo**  |D  G | D/F♯  A | D  G | D/F♯  A | D  G | Bm  A/C♯ |

               |D  G | Em⁷ A |G     | D/F♯ Em⁷ | D     | D       |

               | Cadd⁹ G/B |D    | Cadd⁹ G/B |

         D         Dsus⁴ D      C            G/B  G
**Verse 3**  When I'm tired and  thinking cold

         D          Dsus⁴ D    C      G/B     G
         I hide in my music, forget the day

           D            Dsus⁴ D  C          G/B   G
         And dream of a   girl I used to know

         D          Dsus⁴ D     C           G/B   G
         I close my eyes and she slipped away.

**Link 4**    ‖: D  Dsus⁴ | C  G/B :‖ **x4**

        | Am  Em/G | D | D |

**Chorus 3**    | G  C | Em  D | G  C | Em  D |

       G              C     Em            D
It's more than a feel - ing, *(more than a feel - ing)*

       G           C  Em         Em
When I hear that old song they used to play.___

            D
*(More than a feel - ing)*

G              C       Em             D
I begin dream - ing___ *(more than a feel - ing)*

      G             C      Em  D
'Til I see Mary Ann walk a - way.

                    ***Repeat to fade***
**Outro**    ‖: G  C | Em  D | G  C | Em  D :‖

# MY GENERATION

### Words and Music by Peter Townshend

**Intro**    | G⁵ | F⁵ | G⁵ | F⁵ ‖

**Verse 1**

G              F      G⁵               F⁵
People try to put us down.
*(Talking 'bout my generation.)*

G          F          G⁵             F⁵
Just because we get around.
*(Talking 'bout my generation.)*

G            F       G⁵        F⁵
Things they do look awful c - c - cold.
*(Talking 'bout my generation.)*

G       F         G⁵       F⁵
I hope I die before I get old.
*(Talking 'bout my generation.)*

**Link**

              G⁵
This is my generation,

F⁵            G⁵     F⁵
This is my generation baby.

**Verse 2**

G⁵ N.C.               G⁵      F⁵
Why don't you all f fade away,
*(Talking 'bout my generation.)*

**cont.**
       G⁵    N.C.                     G⁵

Yeah don't try and dig what we all s - s - s - say.

  (G⁵)             F⁵

*(Talking 'bout my generation.)*

      G⁵  N.C.                    G⁵

I'm not tryin' to cause a big s - s - sensation.

  (G⁵)             F⁵

*(Talking 'bout my generation.)*

     G⁵ N.C.                    G⁵

Just talkin' 'bout my g - g - g - gene - ration.

  (G⁵)             F⁵

*(Talking 'bout my generation.)*

        G⁵   F⁵           G⁵       F⁵

My generation, this is my generation baby.

**Bass solo**   ‖: N.C. | N.C. | G | F :‖  **x4**

       | G | F | G | F ‖

        B A N.C.                A               G

**Verse 3**       Why don't you all f - fade away.

                           *(Talking 'bout my generation.)*

       A   N.C.                  A

Yeah don't try and d - dig what we all s - s - s - s - s - s - say.

**cont.**

   (A)               G
*(Talking 'bout my generation.)*

    A  N.C.                  A           G
I'm not tryin' to cause a b-big sensation.
                              *(Talking 'bout my generation.)*

    A  N.C.         A         G
Just talkin' 'bout my g-generation.
                        *(Talking 'bout my generation.)*

**Link 2**

       A    G         A        G
My generation, this is my generation baby

A      G     A      G
  My, my g-generation my, my, my

B♭  A♭  B♭    A♭
My generation.

**Verse 4**

B♭  N.C.      B♭            A♭
People try to put us down.
                *(Talking 'bout my generation.)*

B♭ N.C.              B♭          A♭
  Just because we g-g-g-get around.
                     *(Talking 'bout my generation.)*

B♭   N.C.       B♭          A♭
Things they do look awful c-c-cold.
                   *(Talking 'bout my generation.)*

  B♭   N.C.       B♭          A♭
I hope I die before I get old.
                   *(Talking 'bout my generation.)*

**Link 3**

        B♭    A♭          B♭      A♭
My generation, this is my generation baby,

B♭           A♭            B♭      A♭
My my my my my my my my my gene - g - g - gen - e - ration.

**Outro**

$x10$                              $x8$
‖: C  B♭:‖: C  B♭                           :‖
            This is my generation.
                    *(Talking 'bout my generation.)*

C ‖

# THE ONLY ONE I KNOW

Words and Music by Martin Blunt, Robert Collins,
Timothy Burgess, Jon Baker and Jon Brookes

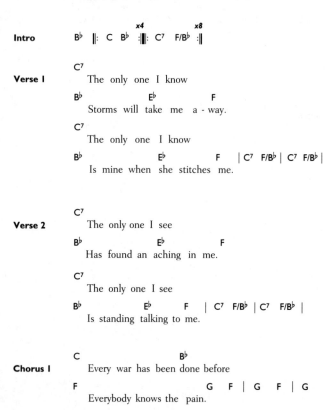

**Intro**   B♭ ‖: C  B♭ :‖ C⁷  F/B♭ :‖
                    x4            x8

**Verse I**
C⁷
    The only one I know
B♭                E♭              F
    Storms will take me a - way.
C⁷
    The only one I know
B♭                    E♭            F  | C⁷  F/B♭ | C⁷  F/B♭ |
    Is mine when she stitches me.

**Verse 2**
C⁷
    The only one I see
B♭                E♭            F
    Has found an aching in me.
C⁷
    The only one I see
B♭                E♭        F   | C⁷  F/B♭ | C⁷  F/B♭ |
    Is standing talking to me.

**Chorus I**
      C                    B♭
    Every war has been done before
F                            G  F | G  F | G
    Everybody knows the pain.

**Verse 3**

C⁷
The only one I know

Bᵇ                Eᵇ              F
Never cries never opens your eyes.

C⁷
The only one I know

Bᵇ             Eᵇ       F  | C⁷ F/Bᵇ | C⁷ F/Bᵇ |
Wide awake, and then she's a - way.

**Verse 4**

C⁷
The only one I see

Bᵇ               Eᵇ          F
Is mine when she walks down the street.

C⁷
The only one I see

Bᵇ          Eᵇ     F  | C⁷ F/Bᵇ | C⁷ F/Bᵇ |
Has carved your way into me.

**Chorus 2**

C                     Bᵇ
Everyone has been burned before

F                     G
Everybody knows the pain.

C                     Bᵇ
Everyone has been burned before,

F                  G  Bᵇ
Everybody knows the pain.

**Link**       | C | C | C | C |

**Instrumental**  ‖: Cm⁷ | Cm⁷ | Eᵇ F | Cm⁷ :‖

**Chorus 3**   *As Chorus 2*

**Outro**     | G F | G F | G F | C ‖

# OWNER OF A LONELY HEART

Words and Music by Jon Anderson, Trevor Rabin, Chris Squire and Trevor Horn

**Intro**      ‖: A5  B5  C5  D5 | A5  B5  C5  D6  G5 :‖

            A5                  B5  C5  D5    G5                       A5

**Verse 1**  Move yourself,         you always live your life

               B5      C5      D5        G5

Never think - ing of the future.

        A5                B5  C5  D5      G5               A5

Prove yourself            you are the move you make,

                B5       C5        D5     G5

Take your chan - ces win or loser.

        A5              B5  C5  D5        G5

See yourself,         you are the steps you take.

        A5    B5  C5         D5           G5

You and you and that's the only way._____

        A5  B5  C5        D5         G5             A5

Shake!   Shake yourself! You're every move you make.

               B5  C5  D5     G5

So the sto  -  ry goes.

        Asus4      B     C     D    G5

**Chorus 1**  Owner of a lonely heart._____

        Asus4      B     C     D    G5

Owner of a lonely heart. *(Much better than a)*

        Asus4      B     C     D    G5

Owner of a broken heart._____

        Asus4      B     C     Dsus2

Owner of a lonely heart.

**Verse 2**

A⁵ B⁵ C⁵      D⁵        G⁵
Say you don't want to chance it⸻

A⁵     B⁵   C⁵      D⁵   G⁵
   You've been hurt so before

A⁵           B⁵ C⁵ D⁵        G⁵
   Watch it now⸻      the eagle   in the sky

A⁵       B⁵      C⁵      D⁵      G⁵
   How he's danc - ing one and only.

A⁵ B⁵ C⁵      D⁵        G⁵
You    lose yourself, no not for pity's sake

A⁵        B⁵   C⁵     D⁵        G⁵
   There's no real reason to be lonely

A⁵        B⁵ C⁵ D⁵          G⁵
Be yourself⸻    give your free   will a chance

A⁵        B⁵ C⁵   D⁵        G⁵
   You've got to want to succeed.


**Chorus 2**

Asus⁴     B    C    D    G⁵
Owner of a lonely heart.⸻

Asus⁴     B    C    D    G⁵
Owner of a lonely heart. *(Much better than a)*

Asus⁴     B    C    D    G⁵
Owner of a broken heart.⸻

Asus⁴     B    C   D A
Owner of a lonely   heart.

**Bridge**

A   Am⁷   G/A   A   Am⁷  G/A A     Am⁷
Own -er of  a  lonely heart.

G/A        A                 Am⁷       G
After my own indecision they confused me so.

My love said  *(owner of a lonely heart)*

A                        Am⁷
Never question your will at all.

G/A      A
In the end you've got to go,

    Am⁷           G/A
Look before you leap,   *(owner of a lonely heart)*

A⁷sus⁴                     G♯⁷  N.C.  G♯⁷
And don't you hesitate at all no, no._____ Yow!

N.C.  G♯⁷  N.C.  G♯⁷  E⁷  F⁷  F♯⁷  G⁷  G♯⁷
                  Ya ya  ya  ya ya

**Guitar solo**  ‖: A⁵  B⁵  C⁵  D⁵  G⁵ :‖: A⁷sus⁴  Csus²  D  Gsus² :‖
                               *x8*                                   *x4*
Yow!

**Chorus 3**

Asus⁴     B  C   D    G⁵
Owner of a lonely heart._

Asus⁴     B  C   D    G⁵
Owner of a lonely heart.  *(Much better than a)*

Asus⁴      B  C D     G⁵  Asus⁴    B   C    D     G⁵
Owner of a broken heart._ Owner of a lonely heart.

**cont.**

Asus⁴     B   C   D    G⁵
Owner of a lonely heart.__

Asus⁴     B   C   D    G⁵
Owner of a lonely heart. *(Much better than a)*

Asus⁴     B   C   D    Asus⁴    B   C   D   A
Owner of a broken heart.__ Owner of a lonely heart.

Am⁷ G/A  A  Am⁷       G/A     A  Am⁷
           Owner of a lonely heart.

**Outro**

    G/A        A
     Sooner or later each conclusion

        Am⁷        G/A  A
Will de - cide the lonely heart. *(Owner of a lonely heart)*

Am⁷ G/A        A
    It will ex - cite, it will delight,

       Am⁷      G/A
It will give a better start *(Owner of a lonely heart)*

     F                   Fm⁷
Don't deceive your free will at all.

E♭/F      F                   Fm⁷  E♭/F
   Don't deceive your free will at all.

*(Owner of a lonely heart)*

                                 **Fade out**
     F                  Fm⁷ E♭/F       F  ‖
Don't deceive your free will at all._____ Just receive it.

# PARANOID

Words and Music by John Osbourne, William Ward,
Terrence Butler and Frank Iommi

**Intro**   $\|:$ E5   | E5   | E5   | E5   $:\|$

**Verse 1**
E5
Finished  with  my  woman
                        D5                          G5   D5   E5   Em7
'Cause  she  couldn't  help  me  with  my  mind.
E5                          E5
People  think  I'm  insane
                  D5                  G5   D5   E5
Because  I  am  frowning  all  the  time.

**Link 1**   $\|:$ E5   | C5  D5 | E5   | E5   $:\|$

**Verse 2**
E5                          E5
All  day  long  I  think  of  things
          D5                          G5   D5   E5   Em7
But  nothing  seems  to  sa -tis -fy.
E5                          E5
Think  I'll  lose  my  mind
                    D5                  G5   D5   E5
If  I  don't  find  something  to  pa - ci - fy.

**Chorus 1**
E5                          E5
                  Can  you  help    me
D5                  D5                  E5
          Occupy  my  brain?
E5                  D5                  D5
          Oh  yeah.

**Link 2**    ‖: E5   | E5   | D5   | G5  D5  E5  Em7 :‖

             E5                   E5

**Verse 3**    I need someone to show me

                  D5          G5  D5   E5

    The things in life that I  can't find.

         E5

    I can't see the things

         E5                     D5        G5   D5   E5

      That make true  hap - piness, I must be  blind.

                                           *x6*

**Guitar solo**  ‖: E5   | E5   | D5   | G5  D5  E5  Em7 :‖

             E5                   E5

**Verse 4**    Make a joke and I will sigh

           D5               G5 D5  E5   Em7

    And you will laugh and I  will cry.

         E5               E5

    Happiness I cannot feel

         D5           G5 D5  E5

    Like love to me is so un - real.

**Link 3**    ‖: E5   | C5  D5 | E5   | E5 .   :‖

         E5                     E5

**Verse 3**    And so as you hear these words

             D5          G5 D5  E5   Em7

    Tel - ling you now of  my state

         E5               E5

    I tell you to enjoy life

         D5           G5 D5  E5   Em7

    I wish I could, but it's too late.

**Outro**    | E5    | E5    | D5    | G5  D5  E5  Em7 |

         | E5    | E5    | D5    | G5  D5  E5 ‖

# ROCKS

Words and Music by Bobby Gillespie, Andrew Innes and Robert Young

**Intro**

‖: A | G D :‖ *x4*

**Verse I**

$A^5$                    $A^5$
Dea - lers keep a - dealin',___ thieves a keep a thievin'.

$G^5$           D         $A^5$
Whores a keep a - whorin',___ junkies keep scorin'.

$A^5$                  $A^5$
Trade is on the meat rack, strip joints full of hunchbacks

$G^5$       D           $A^5$
Bitches keep on bitch - in',___ clap keeps on itchin'.

**Pre-chorus I**

$E^5$                 $G^5$           A
Ain't no use in prayin',___ that's the way it's stayin' baby.

$E^5$            $G^5$                      D
Johnny ain't so crazy,___ he's always got a line for the ladies.

D
Yeah, yeah, yeah.

**Chorus I**

$A^5$                    $G^5$
Get your rocks off,___ get your rocks off honey.

D                   D
Shake 'em down now,___ get 'em off downtown.

$A^5$                  $G^5$
Get your rocks off,___ get your rocks off honey.

D                   D
Shake 'em down now,___ get 'em off downtown.

**Link I**   *As Intro*

        A⁵                       A⁵

**Verse 2**   Creeps a keep a - crawlin',____ drunks a keep a - fallin'.

        G⁵           D         A⁵

Teas - ers keep a teasin',____ Holy Joe's a - preachin'.

        A⁵                  A⁵

Cops a keep a - bustin',____ hustlers keep a - hustlin'.

        G⁵           D         A⁵

Death a keeps a - knockin'____ souls are up for auction.

**Pre-chorus 2**   *As Pre -chorus I*

**Chorus 2**   *As Chorus I*

                      *x4*

**Link 2**   ‖: A⁵ | G⁵   D :‖

**Pre-chorus 3**   *As Pre - chorus I*

        ‖: N.C.

**Chorus 4**      (Get) your rocks off,__ get your rocks off honey,

                                          :‖

Shake 'em down now,____ get 'em off downtown.

        ‖:  A                     G

**Outro**      Get your rocks off,__ get your rocks off honey.

                                    **Repeat to fade**

            D                               D   :‖

Shake 'em down now,____ get 'em off downtown.

# SHEENA IS A PUNK ROCKER

Words and Music by Thomas Erdelyi, John Cummings,
Jeffrey Hyman and Douglas Calvin

**Intro**　　　| C | C | C | C ‖

**Verse 1**

         C
Well, the kids are all hyped up and ready to go

     C
They're ready to go now!

      G
They got their surf and then they're goin' to the

    C
Discothèque a go go.

Am　　　　　F　　　　　Am　　　　　　F
But she just couldn't stay,___ she had to break away.

C　　　　　　　　　　　　　　G
  Well, New York City really has it all.

   G
Oh yeah, oh yeah!___


**Chorus 1**

‖: C　　　　F　　　G　　C
    Sheena is a punk rocker,___

     F　　　G
Sheena is a punk rocker,

C　　　　　F　　G　　　　C F G :‖ C
  Sheena is a punk rocker now!

**Bridge I**

        F
Well she's a punk, punk, a punk rocker,

C                         G
Punk, punk, a punk rocker,_ punk, punk, a punk rocker,

B♭
Punk, punk, a punk rocker!

**Link I**       C

**Verse 2**      *As Verse I*

**Chorus 2**    *As Chorus I*

**Bridge 2**    *As Bridge I*

**Link 2**      *As Link I*

**Chorus 3**

‖: C        F       G
  Sheena is a punk rocker,

    C   F    G
Sheena is a punk rocker,

                     *Repeat to fade*
C       F       G       C F G :‖
Sheena is a punk rocker now!

# SHE SELLS SANCTUARY

Words and Music by Ian Astbury and William Duffy

**Intro**    ‖: D5 | D5 | Csus2 | G5 :‖

                          D                           Csus2             G/B  G5

**Verse 1**    Oh the heads you turn,— make my back burn.

                          D

And   those  heads  that  turn,

            Csus2               G/B      G5

Make  my  back,  make  my  back  burn.

**Link 1**    ‖: D5 | D5 | Csus2 | G5 :‖

                  D5                        Csus2      G/B     Gsus4

**Verse 2**    The sparkle in  your  eyes,— keeps  me   alive.

                  D5

And the  sparkle  in  your  eyes,

    Csus2              G/B     G

Keeps  me  alive, keeps  me  alive.

            D5                  Csus2      G

**Chorus 1**    The  world.—  And  the  world turns  around.

            D5

The  world  and  the  world,  yeah.

**cont.**

    Csus²              G
The world drags me down.

**Link 2**   ‖: D⁵ | D⁵ | Csus² | G⁵ :‖

**Verse 3**

          D                Csus²        G/B   G⁵
Well the heads that turn,— make my back burn.

          D
And those heads that turn,

    Csus²           G/B     G⁵
Make my back, make my back burn.

**Link 3**   ‖: D⁵ | D⁵ | Csus² | G⁵ :‖

**Verse 4**

      D⁵              Csus²       G/B   Gsus⁴
The fire in your eyes,— keeps me alive.

        D⁵            Csus²      G/B   G
And the fire in your eyes,— keeps me alive.

    D⁵            Csus²    G
I'm sure in her you'll find the sanctuary.

    D⁵            Csus²   Gsus⁴/B   Gsus⁴
I'm sure in her you'll find the sanctuary.

                          D⁵        Csus²                    G/B      G
**Chorus 2**    And  the  world,___ the  world  turns  around.

                              D⁵
              And  the  world  and  the  world,

                  Csus²                    G
              The  world  drags  me  down.

          ‖:              D⁵
              And the world, and  the  world, and  the  world,

                  Csus²                  G :‖
              The  world  drags  me  down.


                  D⁵                        D⁵      Csus²      G
**Link 4**               Ah___ yeah,___ yeah  yeah,


**Chorus 3**    *As Chorus 2*


                  D⁵        Csus²              G
**Outro**        Yeah_____ yeah,  yeah

                                                              ⌢
                  D⁵                  Csus²                  G/B    G⁵   D⁵ ‖
              Sanctuary  yeah,_____  sanctuary  yeah.

# SMELLS LIKE TEEN SPIRIT

Words and Music by Kurt Cobain, Chris Novoselic and David Grohl

**Intro**    ‖: Fsus⁴    B♭    | A♭sus⁴    D♭    :‖

‖: F5    B♭5    | A♭5    D♭5    :‖ **x6**

**Verse I**

F5        B♭5    A♭5      D♭5
Load up on guns,— and bring— your friends

F5        B♭5    A♭5      D♭5
It's fun— to lose— and to— pretend.

F5        B♭5    A♭5      D♭5
She's o - ver - bored and self - assured,

F5        B♭5    A♭5      D♭5
Oh no,— I know— a dirt - y word.

**Pre-chorus I**

F5    B♭5    A♭5    D♭5
Hel - lo,— hel - lo,— hel - lo, how low?

F5    B♭5    A♭5    D♭5
Hel - lo,— hel - lo,— hel - lo, how low?

F5    B♭5    A♭5    D♭5
Hel - lo,— hel - lo,— hel - lo, how low?

F5    B♭5    A♭5    D♭5
Hel - lo, hel - lo, hel - lo. With the lights

**Chorus 1**

| Fsus⁴ | | B♭ | A♭sus⁴ | D♭ |
|---|---|---|---|---|
| out,_____ | | it's less | dang -'rous.. | Here we are_ |

| Fsus⁴ | | B♭ | A♭sus⁴ | D♭ |
|---|---|---|---|---|
| _ now, | | entertain__ us. | | I feel stu - |

| Fsus⁴ | B♭ | A♭sus⁴ | | D♭ |
|---|---|---|---|---|
| - pid____ and conta - gious, | | here we are____ |

| Fsus⁴ | | B♭ | A♭sus⁴ | D♭ |
|---|---|---|---|---|
| _ now, | | entertain__ us. | | A mul - la - |

| Fsus⁴ | | B♭ | A♭sus⁴ | D♭ |
|---|---|---|---|---|
| - to,____ | | an albi - no, | | a mosqui - |

| Fsus⁴ | | B♭ | A♭sus⁴ | D♭ |
|---|---|---|---|---|
| - to,____ | | my libi - do. | | Yay. |

**Bridge**

‖: F⁵ E⁵ F⁵ G♭⁵ N.C | F⁵ E⁵ F⁵ B♭⁵ A♭⁵ :‖
　　　　Yay.

‖: F⁵ B♭⁵ | A♭⁵ D♭⁵ :‖

**Verse 2**

| F⁵ | | B♭⁵ | A♭⁵ | D♭⁵ |
|---|---|---|---|---|
| I'm worse at what____ | | I____ do best,____ |

| F⁵ | | B♭⁵ | A♭⁵ | D♭⁵ |
|---|---|---|---|---|
| _and for____ this gift____ | | I feel____ blessed. |

| F⁵ | B♭⁵ | A♭⁵ | | D♭⁵ |
|---|---|---|---|---|
| _ Our lit -tle group has____ | | al - ways been____ |

| F⁵ | B♭⁵ | A♭⁵ | | D♭⁵ |
|---|---|---|---|---|
| _ and al - ways will____ | | until____ the end. |

**Pre-chorus 2** *As Pre-chorus 1*

**Chorus 2** *As Chorus 1*

**Guitar solo**  ‖:Fsus⁴  B♭ | A♭sus⁴  D♭ :‖  *x8*  F⁵ ‖
*with feedback*

F⁵              B♭⁵              A♭⁵              D♭⁵
**Chorus 3**   And  I  for - get____  just  why____  I  taste,__

F⁵              B♭⁵              A♭⁵              D♭⁵
__ Oh yeah,__  I  guess____  it makes__ me  smile.__

F⁵              B♭⁵              A♭⁵              D♭⁵
__ I found it hard,_____  it was hard__ to find,__

F⁵              B♭⁵              A♭⁵              D♭⁵
__ Oh well,__ whatev - er,  nev - er  mind.__

**Pre-chorus 3**  *As Pre-chorus 1*  (With the lights)

Fsus⁴              B♭              A♭sus⁴              D♭
**Chorus 3**   out,_____  it's  less  dang -'rous.__  Here we are

Fsus⁴              B♭              A♭sus⁴              D♭
__  now,  entertain_____  us.   I feel stu-

Fsus⁴      B♭   A♭sus⁴         D♭
- pid__and contagious,__  here we__ are____

Fsus⁴              B♭              A♭sus⁴              D♭
__  now,       entertain_____  us.   A mul - la -

Fsus⁴      B♭   A♭sus⁴      D♭        Fsus⁴
- to,__  an  albi - no,   a mosqui - to,__

B♭      A♭sus⁴         D♭        ‖: Fsus⁴              B♭
my libi - do.   A  deni  -  al,   a  deni

A♭sus⁴                        D♭
- al,_____       a   deni  -

Fsus⁴              B♭   A♭sus⁴              D♭      :‖
- al,   a   deni - al,____    a   deni -

F⁵_____  F⁵_____  F⁵ ‖
- al!_____       *(with feedback)*

# SONG 2

Words and Music by Damon Albarn, Graham Coxon,
Alex James and David Rowntree

**Tune lowest string to D**

**Intro**  ‖: F⁵   E♭5 |A♭5  B♭5  C⁵ :‖

                F⁵   E♭5   A♭5  B♭5  C⁵
    Woo - ooh!

                F⁵   E♭5   A♭5  B♭5  C⁵
    Woo - ooh!

                F⁵   E♭5   A♭5  B♭5  C⁵
    Woo - ooh!

                F⁵   E♭5   A♭5  B♭5  C⁵
    Woo - ooh!

                    F⁵              E♭5  A♭5  B♭5  C⁵
**Verse 1**  I  got  my  head  checked

                    F⁵              E♭5  A♭5  B♭5  C⁵
    By a  jumbo  jet,

                    F⁵              E♭5  A♭5  B♭5  C⁵
    It  wasn't  easy,

                    F⁵              E♭5  A♭5  B♭5  C⁵
    But  nothing  is,                          no.

|        |     | F5   | Eb5 |        | Ab5  |     | Bb5 | C5 |
| ------ | --- | ---- | --- | ------ | ---- | --- | --- | -- |

**Chorus I**    Woo - hoo!    When I  feel hea - vy    metal.

            F5       Eb5              Ab5       Bb5  C5

Woo - hoo!        And I'm pins and I'm  needles,

            F5       Eb5              Ab5       Bb5  C5

Woo - hoo!        Well  I  lie and I'm easy,

F5                      Ab5                     Db

All of the time but I'm  never  sure  why I  need you,

Db5

    Pleased  to meet you.

**Link I**    ‖: F5    Eb5  | Ab5    Bb5 C5 :‖

                    F5          Eb5 Ab5  Bb5 C5

**Verse 2**    I got my head  down

                F5        Eb5 Ab5  Bb5 C5

When I  was young,

              F5    Eb5 Ab5  Bb5 C5

It's not  my  prob - lem.

                F5   Eb5 Ab5  Bb5 C5

It's not  my      prob  -  lem.____

**Chorus 2**    *As Chorus I*

**Outro**    ‖: F5    Eb5  |  Ab5    Bb5 C5    :‖ *x3*

                                    Yeah,  yeah.

  | F5    Eb5  |  Ab5    Bb5 C5  | N.C.    ‖

                               Oh,  yeah.

# SMOKE ON THE WATER

### Words and Music by Jon Lord, Ritchie Blackmore, Ian Gillan, Roger Glover and Ian Paice

**Intro**  ‖: G5 B♭5 C5 | G5 B♭5 D♭5 C5 | G5 B♭5 C5 | B♭5 G5 :‖ x6

**Verse I**
      Gm
We all came down to Montreux

              F     Gm
On the lake Gene - va shoreline.

  Gm
    To make records with the mobile.

F          Gm
    We didn't have much time.

  Gm
    Frank Zappa and the Mothers

            F    Gm
Were at the best place around.

  Gm
    But some stupid with a flare gun

            F     Gm
Burned the place to the ground

**Chorus I**
  C             A♭   Gm
Smoke on the water,___ fire in the sky.

  C        A♭
Smoke on the water.

**Link I**  ‖: G5 B♭5 C5 | G5 B♭5 D♭5 C5 | G5 B♭5 C5 | B♭5 G5 :‖

**Verse 2**

Gm
They burned down the gambling house

F
It died with an awful sound,

Gm
Funky Claude was running in and out

F          Gm
He was pulling kids out the ground.

When it was all over

F          Gm
We had to find another place

But Swiss time was running out

F          Gm
It seemed that we would lose the race.

**Chorus 2**   *As Chorus 1*

**Link 2**   *As Link 1*

                      *x4*
**Guitar solo**   ‖: Gm   Cm   Gm :‖   Cm   F   Gm

**Link 3**   *As Link 1*

**Verse 3**

Gm
      We ended up at the Grand Hotel

     F     Gm
It was empty cold and bare

       Gm
But with the rolling truck stones thing just outside, yeah!

F        Gm
   Making our music there.

    Gm
With a few red lights and few old beds

      F      Gm
We made a place to sweat

No matter what we get out of this

    F      Gm
I know, we'll never forget.

**Chorus 3**    *As Chorus 1*

**Link 4**    *As Link 1*

       *Repeat to fade*
**Outro**    ‖: *As Link 1* :‖

# START ME UP

Words and Music by Mick Jagger and Keith Richards

**Intro**    C ‖ C F  C | F  C F | B♭      | B♭    C |

| C  F   C | C  F  C F | B♭ E♭/B♭ B♭ | B♭ E♭/B♭ B♭

**Verse I**

    C   C  F     C
If you start me  up,

C F   C        F        B♭       B♭  E♭/B♭
    If you start me  up, I'll  never stop.

        C  F     C
If you start me  up,

C F   C        F        B♭
      If you start me  up, I'll  never stop.

         C  F       C
I've  been  running  hot, uh,

C F        C      F       B♭         B♭
      The job  we're riggin' now don't blow my top.

        C  F
If you start me  up, oh,

C F  C      F        B♭
      If you start me up, I'll  never stop, never  stop

B♭
Never stop, I'll  never stop.

**Chorus I**

C                        F5    E♭5 D5 C5
   You make a grown  man  cry.

C                        F5    E♭5 D5 C5
   You make a grown  man  cry.

**cont.**

    C                         F      E♭ D C
You make a grown man cry.

C       Csus⁴   C       Csus⁴   C
Spread out the oil,   the gasoline,

C                    E♭5 D5 C5 E♭5 D5   C5
I wanna smooth ride in a mean,    mean machine.

| C  F  C | C  F C  F | B♭       E♭/B♭  B♭  E♭/B♭ | B♭
                           Start it up.


**Verse 2**

        C          F        C
You   can start me up,

C F      C       F      B♭
    Kick on the starter, give it all you've got,

        B♭
You've got, you've got.

  C    F   C   F     C    F         B♭
I can't compete,   with the riders in the other heats.

      C     F     C
If you rough it up,

C      F        C         F
     'N'  if  you     like    it you  can
B♭
Slide it up, start it up,   start it up, start it up.


**Chorus 2**

C5                           F5  E♭5 D5 C5
   Don't make a grown man cry.

C5                       F5  E♭5 D5 C5
   Don't make a grown man cry.

C5                           F5  E♭5 D5 C5
   Don't make a grown man cry.

C     Csus⁴  C     Csus⁴  C
   My eyes dilate, my lips go green,

C                         E♭5    D5  E♭5     D5
   My hands are greasy, she's a mean,   mean machine.

**Verse 3**

         C      F     C
Mm, start me  up...
C F    C F      $B^\flat$
    Now   give it all you've got, you've got to
$B^\flat$
Never, never, never stop.
C      F        C   F       C    F
Start  it  up,  ooh!         Oh,  baby,   why don't ya
$B^\flat$
Start it up, (start it up, start it up),  never,  never,  never...

**Chorus 3**

C                          $F^5$     $E^{\flat 5}$ $D^5$ $C^5$
  You make a  grown man  cry.
$C^5$                   $F^5$     $E^{\flat 5}$ $D^5$ $C^5$
  You make a grown man  cry.
$C^5$                 $F^5$     $E^{\flat 5}$ $D^5$ $C^5$
  You make a grown man  cry.
C     Csus⁴   C     Csus⁴  C
Ride like the wind, at  double speed,
$C^5$                   $E^{\flat 5}$      $D^5$  $C^5$
  I'll  take you places that you've  never,  never seen.
| C     F     C   | C F C  F | $B^\flat$              | $B^\flat$

**Verse 4**

          C      F     C
Once you start it up,
C F    C       F         $B^\flat$
    Let me tell you, we will never stop, we'll never  stop,
     $B^\flat$                    $C^5$
We'll never, never, never stop.
C      F    C   | C    F    C      F
Start me up,
    $B^\flat$                  $B^\flat$   $C^5$
We'll never stop, never stop.

**Outro**

C     F    C  F      C    F     $B^\flat$
  You,  you,  you make a grown man cry.
C F C  F      C    F     $B^\flat$     $E^\flat/B^\flat$  $B^\flat$
  You, you make a dead man  come.      *repeat to fade*
‖: C  F  C    F      C    F    $B^\flat$           C :‖
  You,  you,  you make a dead man  come.   Yeah, and

# TALK

Words and Music by Guy Berryman, William Champion, Christopher Martin,
Jonathan Buckland, Karl Bartos, Ralf Hütter and Emil Schult

**Intro**   ‖: Gm   | Gm   | Gm   | Gm   | Gm  F/A :‖ Gm   ‖

| E♭   | Gm  B♭ | E♭   | Gm  B♭ |

| E♭   | Gm  B♭ | E♭   | Fsus⁴  F ‖

**Verse 1**

E♭              Gm      B♭      E♭      Gm    B♭
    Oh brother I can't, I  can't get through.
          E♭                    Gm
I've  been  trying hard  to reach you
B♭          E♭                      Fsus⁴      F
'Cos I don't    know what to do.
E♭              Gm      B♭      E♭    Gm    B♭
    Oh brother I can't believe  it's true,
        E♭                  Gm  B♭      E♭          Fsus⁴  F
I'm so scared about the future and I want to talk to you,
              E♭              Fsus⁴  F
Oh I want  to talk to you._____

**Link 1**   | Gm⁷   | Gm⁷   | Gm⁷   | Gm⁷   |

**Chorus 1**

              E♭                  Gm              B♭  E♭ Gm B♭
You could take a picture of  something you see
E♭              Gm          B♭  E♭ Gm B♭
In  the future,  where will  I  be?
              E♭                  Gm              B♭  E♭ Gm B♭
You could  climb  a  ladder up  to the sun
      E♭              Gm      B♭
Or write  a  song  no -body had  sung
      E♭              Fsus⁴                  F
Or do something that's never been done.

**Link 2**  | Gm⁷  | Gm⁷  | Gm⁷  | Gm⁷  |

**Verse 2**

    E♭           Gm    B♭    E⁵    Gm    B♭
Are you lost,   or  incom - plete?

        E♭       Gm    B♭       E♭              Fsus⁴ F
Do you feel like a puzzle, you can't find your missing piece.

       E♭         Gm    B♭    E♭  Gm  B♭
Tell me  how you feel._____

      E♭            Gm B♭   E♭          Fsus⁴
Well I feel like they're talk - ing in a language I don't speak

 F             E♭         Fsus⁴    F
And they're talk - ing it to me._____

**Link 3**  | Gm  | Gm  | Gm  | Gm  |

**Chorus 2**

       E♭              Gm             B♭ E♭ Gm B♭
So you take a picture of something you see

    E♭        Gm        B♭ E♭ Gm B♭
In the future, where will I  be?

       E♭            Gm          B♭ E♭ Gm B♭
You could climb a ladder up to the sun

    E♭           Gm       B♭
Or write  a  song  no -body had sung

    E♭            Fsus⁴        F
Or do something that's never been done.

 E♭              Fsus⁴     F
Do___ something that's never been done.

**Link 3**  | Gm⁷   | Gm⁷   | Gm⁷   | Gm⁷   ‖ Cm   | E♭   |

| Gm   | F   | Cm   | E♭   | Gm   | F   |

**Guitar solo**  ‖: Cm   | E♭   | Gm   | F   :‖ E♭   | Gm   B♭   |

| E♭   | Gm   B♭ | E♭   | Gm   B♭ | E♭   | F   |

           E♭

**Outro**  So you  don't know where  you're  going

        Gm⁷   B♭  E♭  Gm⁷  B♭

And you want to talk,  you

E♭                   Gm⁷   B♭  E♭  Gm⁷  B♭

feel  like  you're  going  where  you've  been  before.

        E♭

You'll  tell  anyone  who'll  listen,

        Gm⁷   B♭   E♭   Gm⁷   B♭

But  you  feel  ignored.

   E♭                Gm⁷        B♭

And  nothing's  really  making  any  sense  at  all.     Let's

E♭       F          E♭maj⁷     F      Gm  ‖

talk,  let's  talk.___  Let's  talk,   let's  talk.____

# TEENAGE DIRTBAG

Words and Music by Brendan Brown

**Tune lowest string to D**

**Intro**     ‖: E     Bsus⁴  |  E     A     :‖

**Verse I**
          E               Bsus⁴
Her   name     is   Noel,___
E               A
I   have  a   dream___  about   her.
E              Bsus⁴
She   rings   my   bell___
     E              A
Got   gym   class   in   half___  an   hour.
E              Bsus⁴
Oh   how   she   rocks___
     E            A
In   keds   and   tube   socks.
     C♯m⁷      Asus²        Bsus⁴
But   she   doesn't   know   who   I   am,
     C♯m⁷        Asus²    Bsus⁴
And she   doesn't   give     a   damn     about me.

**Chorus I**
       E⁵      A⁵        B⁵    C♯  G♯⁵
'Cos   I'm   just   a   teenage   dirtbag   ba - by,   yeah.
E⁵       A⁵       B⁵    C♯⁵  G♯⁵
I'm   just   a   teenage   dirtbag   ba - by.
E⁵       A⁵      B⁵  C♯⁵  G♯⁵    E⁵    A⁵
Listen   to   Iron   Mai - den   maybe   with   me,   ooh.
|  B⁵   C♯⁵  G♯⁵      |  A⁵  B⁵   |

**Link I**     *As Intro*

**Verse 2**

    E                Bsus⁴
Her   boyfriend's a  dick,

    E            A
He brings  a  gun to  school and

E            Bsus⁴
He'd simply kick

    E            A
My  ass  if  he  knew___ the  truth.

    E          Bsus⁴
He lives on my  block

       E         A
And he drives an I - rok.

        C♯m⁷  Asus²        Bsus⁴
But he doesn't know who I  am,

        C♯m⁷   Asus²  Bsus⁴
And he doesn't give a  damn about me.

**Chorus 2**    *As Chorus 1*

**Bridge**

‖: E    Asus²      E  Asus²    E   Asus²
         Oh yeah         dirtbag.

    C♯5  G♯5        A5          B5      :‖
No, she doesn't know what she's  missin'.

**Link 2**    | E  Bsus⁴ | E  A ‖

**Verse 3**

    E            Bsus⁴
Man I feel like mould

E            A
It's prom night and   I am  lonely.

    E          Bsus⁴
Lo and  behold,

**cont.**

E            A
She's walkin' ov - er to me,

E          Bsus⁴
This must be fake

   E       A
My lip starts to shake

C♯m⁷         Asus²    Bsus⁴
How does she know who I am?

    C♯m⁷      Asus²    Bsus⁴
And why does she give__ a damn about me?

**Chorus 3**

          E⁵    A⁵      B⁵  C♯⁵   G♯⁵
I've got two tickets to Iron Mai - den, ba - by.

E⁵            A⁵
Come with me Fri - day,

   B⁵    C♯⁵  G♯⁵
Don't say may - be.

E⁵       A⁵     B⁵    C♯⁵
I'm just a teen - age dirt - bag ba - by,

G♯⁵ E⁵    A⁵  B⁵ C♯⁵ G♯⁵ | A⁵ B⁵ |
Like you, ooh.

**Bridge 2**

‖: E  Asus²        E  Asus²       E  Asus²
        Oh yeah         dirtbag.

    C♯⁵ G♯⁵       A⁵        B⁵       :‖
No, she doesn't know what she's missin'.

**Outro**    | E⁵  B⁵ | E⁵  A⁵  G♯ |

            | E⁵   B⁵   G♯ | E⁵  A⁵  G♯  F♯ | G♯  F♯ ‖

# THIS CHARMING MAN

Words and Music by Steven Morrissey and Johnny Marr

**Tune guitar down a semitone**

**Intro**    A E Asus E | F#m⁷ C#m | Bm⁷ | D C#m⁷ | A F#m E A | C#m⁷

**Verse 1**

N.C.     Bm⁷            D    C#m⁷    A F#m
Punctured bicycle___ on a hillside desolate

E     A         E       Bm⁷    D
Will nature make a man of me  yet?

C#m⁷       A       A    E     Bm⁷   D C#m⁷
When in this charming car this charm - ing man.

        A               F#m
Why pamper life's complexities

    E    A                  E       Bm⁷
When the leather runs smooth on the passenger seat?___

D   C#m⁷         A
     I would go out tonight

F#m   E   A        E       Bm⁷   D   C#m⁷
But I haven't got a stitch to wear,

      A             F#m
This man said "It's gruesome

        E          E      Bm⁷   D   C#m⁷
That someone so handsome should care."___

**Bridge 1**

Dmaj⁹     C#m⁷/E           F#m⁷
    A jumped    up pantry   boy___
          B⁹          Dmaj⁹
Who never knew his place,

    C#m/B   F#m⁷
He said re - turn the ring

**cont.**

    Dmaj⁹          C♯m⁷/E   F♯m⁷  B⁹
He knows so much a - bout these things

    Dmaj⁹          C♯m⁷/B   F♯m⁷
He knows so much a - bout these things.

**Verse 2**

N.C.        A
  I would go out tonight

F♯m  E  A      E      Bm⁷  D  C♯m⁷
But I haven't got a stitch to wear,

   A               F♯m
This man said "It's gruesome

  E  A      E         Bm⁷  D  C♯m⁷
That someone so handsome should care."_____

 A F♯m E A              Bm⁷    D
Na na na na na na na,__ this charm - ing man,

C♯m⁷  A      F♯m E A  E    Bm⁷  D  C♯m
Oh na na na na na na na__ this charm - ing man,__ ah!

**Bridge 2**   *As Bridge 1*

**Outro**

    Dmaj⁹  C♯m⁷/E  F♯m⁷  B⁹    Dmaj⁹  C♯m/B
He knows so much a - bout these things._____

F♯m⁷  Dmaj⁹ | C♯m⁷/E  F♯m⁷ | B⁹  Dmaj⁹ | C♯m/B  F♯m⁷ ‖

# WHEN THE SUN GOES DOWN

### Words and Music by Alex Turner

**Intro**

B                  D#

Who's that girl there?

Emaj⁷

I wonder what went wrong

D#

So that she had to roam the streets.

Emaj⁷

She dunt do major credit cards,

D#m

I doubt she does receipts,

C#m         F#⁷   E⁷   D#m  C#m D#m

It's all not quite legitimate.

B                   D#

And what a scummy man,

Emaj⁷

Just give him half a chance

D#m

I'll bet he'll rob you if he can.

Emaj⁷

Can see it in his eyes yeah,

D#m

That he's got a driving ban,

C#m         F#⁷   E⁷   D#m  C#m  D#m

Amongst some other offences.

**cont.**

G#m                      D#m
      And I've seen him with girls of the night,

G#m                 D#m
And he told Roxanne to put on her red light.

G#m                 D#m
     It's all infected, but he'll be alright,

         C#m             D#m      E7    F#7
'Cause he's a scum - bag don't you know,

N.C.
I said he's a scumbag don't you

**Link I**

                                                       x3
| Bm (N.C.) | (N.C.) G F# ‖: Bm   (N.C.) | (N.C.) G F# :‖
know!                                            x3
| G     F#   | B D E F# ‖: G    F# | Bm  :‖ G    F# |

**Verse I**

Bm                           G      F#
      Although you're trying not to lis - ten,

Bm                     G     F#
      Overt your eyes and staring at the ground

Bm                     G      F#
      She makes a subtle pro - posi - tion,

Bm                   G       F#
      "I'm sorry love, I'll have to turn you down."

Bm                    G      F#
      Oh he must be up to some - thing,

Bm                          G       F#
      What are the chances, sure it's more than likely.

Bm                    G      F#
      I've got a feeling in my sto - mach,

Bm                       G    F#
      I start to wonder what his story might be,

        Bm
What his story might be.

**Chorus 1**

              Em          F#m              Bm
Yeah, 'cause they said it changes when the sun goes down,

       Em         F#m          Bm
Yeah they said it changes when the sun goes down,

        Em        F#m          Bm
Well, they said it changes when the sun goes down

        Em  F#m Bm    A  F#m
Around here.___    Around_ here.  Ah.

**Link 2**    ‖: G  F# | B  D  E  F# :‖

**Verse 2**

Bm                       G    F#
   Look, here comes a Ford Mon - deo,
Bm                G      F#
   Isn't he Mister In - conspic - uous?
Bm                   G    F#
   And he don't even have to say 'owt
Bm                  G      F#
   She's in the stance ready to get picked up.
Bm                     G    F#
   Bet she's delighted when she sees    him,
Bm                  G       F#
   Pulling in and giving her the eye.
Bm                          G    F#
   Because she must be fucking  freez - ing,

Bm                        G      F#
   Scantily clad beneath the  clear night sky,

   Bm
It doesn't stop in the winter, no.

**Chorus 2**    *As Chorus 1*

**Chorus 3**

       Em           F#m                Bm
Well they said it changes when the sun goes down

Em       F#m       Bm
Over the river going out of town.

Em          F#m              Bm
They said it changes when the sun goes down

         Em    F#m Bm     A    F#
Around   here.__     Around__ here. Oh.

**Outro**

B                        D#7
     And what a scummy man,

Emaj7
Just give him half a chance

       D#m
I'll bet he'll rob  you if he can.

     Emaj7
Can see it in his eyes yeah,

     D#m
That he's got a nasty plan.

           C#m        D#m   E7  F#7 F#7b9  F#7  B
I hope you're not involved at all.

# WILD THING

### Words and Music by Chip Taylor

**Intro**  | A  D | E ‖

          A       D E D          A        D    E

**Chorus I**  Wild  thing____  you  make  my  heart  sing,

         D          A       D      E    D

         You  make  ev - 'rything  groo - vy.

         A       D  E  Gsus⁴/A  A  Gsus⁴/A

         Wild  thing.

**Verse I**

         A                        Gsus⁴/A  A  Gsus⁴/A

         Wild  thing____  I  think  I  love  you.

         A                 Gsus⁴/A  A  Gsus⁴/A

         But  I  wanna  know  for  sure,

                            Gsus⁴/A  A  Gsus⁴/A  A

         So  come  on  and  a - hold me  tight____  I  love  you.

**Link I**  ‖: A  D | E  D :‖

         A       D E D          A         D   E

**Chorus 2**  Wild  thing____  you  make  my  heart  sing,

         D          A       D     E D A       D   E

         You  make  ev - 'rything  groo - vy.____  Wild  thing.

**Ocarina solo** ‖: A  D | E  D :‖ ×3  A  D | E  Gsus⁴/A | A  Gsus⁴/A |

          A                                  Gsus⁴/A  A  Gsus⁴/A

**Verse 2**   Wild  thing___  I think you move me.

          A                          Gsus⁴/A  A  Gsus⁴/A
          But  I  wanna  know  for  sure,

          A                            Gsus⁴/A  A  Gsus⁴/A
          So  come on  and  a - hold me tight

          A
          You  move  me...

**Link 2**     | A  D | E  D | A  D | E

          A       D E D          A        D E

**Chorus 3**   Wild  thing,___  you  make  my  heart  sing,

          D      A      D    E D
          You  make  everything  groovy

          A       D E D          A       D E D
          Wild  thing,      c'mon  c'mon,  wild  thing,

                                    *Repeat to fade*
                          ‖: A       D E D :‖
          Shake  it,  shake  it     wild  thing.

# ZIGGY STARDUST

Words and Music by David Bowie

**Intro**
| G    D | Cadd⁹ G/B A⁷sus⁴ |
                 Oh!
| G    D | Cadd⁹ G/B A⁷sus⁴ | G   D | Cadd⁹ G/B A⁷sus⁴ |
                                Ooh yeah,___
| G    D | Cadd⁹ G/B A⁷sus⁴ ||
       Aah!

**Verse 1**

       G

          Ziggy played guitar,

Bm                            C

Jamming good with Weird and Gilly

               G/B    C    A⁷/C♯

And the spiders  from Mars.___

       D

          He played it left hand,

G                  Em                       A⁷

          But made it too far,___  became the spe - cial man,

               C          G/B   Am⁷

Then we were Ziggy's band.

**Verse 2**

       G

          Ziggy really sang,

Bm                                       C

          Screwed up eyes, and screwed down hair - do

               G/B    C    A⁷/C♯

Like some cat from Ja - pan,

       D                         G

          He could lick 'em by smil - ing,

                        Em

He could leave 'em to hang,

             A⁷

They came on so loaded man,

           C

Well hung, and snow white tan.

**Chorus 1**

Am      G            F          G
      So where were the spi - ders,
Am           G            F          G
      While the fly tried to break our balls?
Am           G            F     G
      With just the beer light to guide us,
          D
    So we bitched about his fans,
                 E
    And should we crush his sweet hands? Oh!

**Link 1**

| G  D | Cadd⁹ G/B A⁷sus⁴ | G  D | Cadd⁹ G/B A⁷sus⁴ |

**Verse 3**

G
      Ziggy played for time,
Bm                        C          G/B  C  A⁷/C♯
    Jiving us that we were voo - doo. The kids were just crass
D              G
    He was the nazz,   with God given ass,
Em          A⁷                        C
    He took it all too far, but the boy, could he play guitar.

**Chorus 2**

Am       G             F         G
      Making love with his e - go,
Am       G         F          G
      Ziggy sucked up into    his mind, oh,
Am       G         F
      Like a leper messi - ah,
          G  D
    When the kids had killed the man
                E
    I had to break up the band.   Oh!

**Outro**

| G  D | Cadd⁹ G/B A⁷sus⁴ | G  D | Cadd⁹ G/B A⁷sus⁴   |
                                                   Ooh yeah

| G  D | Cadd⁹ G/B A⁷sus⁴ | G  D |

| Cadd⁹             | G ‖
    Ziggy played guitar.

# YOU SHOOK ME ALL NIGHT LONG

Words and Music by Brian Johnson, Angus Young and Malcom Young

**Intro**  | G | G | D⁵ | D⁵ |

| G | G | D | D ‖

‖: G⁵ | C  G⁵ | D⁵ | G⁵  D⁵  G⁵  D⁵ :‖

**Verse I**
                G⁵                               C       G⁵
She was a fast machine, she kept her motor clean,

        D⁵                            G⁵   D⁵   G⁵
She was the best damn woman that I've ever seen.

       D⁵     G⁵               C       G⁵   D⁵
She had the sightless eyes, tellin' me no lies

                            G⁵    D⁵ G⁵
Knocking me out with those American thighs.

D⁵    G⁵                         C        G   C   G
Taking more than her share, had me fighting for air

D                         G⁵       D⁵    G⁵
She told me to come but I was already there.

D⁵    G⁵                   C       G   C
'Cos the walls start shaking, the earth was quaking,

G   D                         G⁵/D   D
My mind was aching and we were making it.

**Chorus I**
        G⁵              Csus²  G⁵/B  D⁵
And you shook me all    night long,

        G⁵              Csus²  G⁵/B  D⁵
And you shook me all    night long,

**Verse 2**

        G⁵                   C       G⁵
Working double time on the seduction line,

        D⁵                  G⁵  D⁵   G⁵
She's one of a kind, she's just mine, all mine.

D⁵   G⁵            C       G⁵
Wanted no applause, just another course,

       D⁵          G⁵       D⁵   G⁵
Made a meal of me and come back for more.

D⁵   G⁵           C     G      C
Had to cool me down, to take another round,

G   D                 G⁵  D⁵   G⁵
Now I'm back in the ring to take another swing.

D⁵   G⁵         C      G C
God, the walls was shaking, the earth was quaking,

G   D         G⁵/D       D  G⁵/D  D
My mind was aching and we were making it.

**Chorus 2**

       G⁵          Csus²  G⁵/B  D⁵
And you shook me all     night long,

        G⁵         Csus²  G⁵/B  D⁵            G⁵/B
Yeah, you shook me all     night long.   Knocked me out,

        G⁵         Csus²  G⁵/B  D⁵   Csus   G⁵/B
I said you shook me all     night long,— you had me shaking

       G⁵          Csus²  G⁵/B  D   G⁵/B
And you shook me all     night long,

                        D
Yeah, you shook me,— well you took me.

**Guitar solo**   $\|$: G$^5$   Csus$^2$ | G$^5$/B   D$^5$ | D$^5$   Csus$^2$ |

| G$^5$/B   G$^5$ | G$^5$   Csus$^2$ | G$^5$/B   D$^5$ |

| D$^5$   Csus$^2$ | G$^5$/B :$\|$

*Repeat to fade*

**Chorus 3**   $\|$: *As Chorus 2* :$\|$